HEADSTART

WORKBOOK

BEGINNER

Tim Falla

OXFORD UNIVERSITY PRESS

ACKNOWLEDGEMENTS

The publishers would like to thank the following teachers and institutions for commenting on this edition of the manuscript:

Jeremy Page
International House, London
Tim Eyres
Godmer House, Oxford
Sara Evans
Eliane Paim
SBCI-Rio

The publishers would like to thank the following for their permission to reproduce photographs and copyright material:

Slide File Ltd

Location photography by:

John Walmsley

Studio photography by:

John Walmsley

Illustrations by:

Helen Ball
Katherine Baxter
Valerie Falla
Joanna Kerr
Keith Shaw

Thanks to the following for their time and assistance:

Steve Malaigh at Barclays Bank, Oxford

Oxford University Press, Great Clarendon Street,
Oxford OX2 6DP

Oxford New York
Athens Auckland Bangkok Bogotá Buenos Aires
Calcutta Cape Town Chennai Dar es Salaam
Delhi Florence Hong Kong Istanbul Karachi
Kuala Lumpur Madrid Melbourne Mexico City
Mumbai Nairobi Paris São Paulo Singapore
Taipei Tokyo Toronto Warsaw

and associated companies in
Berlin Ibadan

OXFORD and OXFORD ENGLISH
are trade marks of Oxford University Press

ISBN 0 19 435722 8

© Oxford University Press

First published 1995
2000 impression
Printing ref. (last digit): 6 5 4 3 2 1

Designed by
Keith Shaw
Threefold Design
Oxford

Printed in China

CONTENTS

UNIT 1

1 `T1` **Put the sentences in the correct order.**

☐ Fine, thanks. And you?

☐ Hi, John. How are you?

☐ Very well, thanks.

`1` Hello, Ann.

2 `T2` **Put the words in the correct order.**

Example
thanks / Very / well
Very well thanks.

a How / you / are ?

_____

b name's / John / My

_____

c name / What's / your ?

_____

d Tom / is / This

_____

c This _____ .

d _____

e _____

f _____

3 **Read and write.**

a *This is a computer.*
_____

b _____
_____ taxi.

g _____
_____

h _____
_____

4 **T3** **Read and write.**

a **Sue Parker**   Hello. My _name's_ Sue Parker.

           What's your _____ ?

   Tony Brown   Tony. Tony Brown.

b **Jim**   Hello, Sara. _____ are you?

   Sara   _____ , thanks. And _____ ?

   Jim   _____ , _____ .

c **Helen**   Toros, this is Steven.

        Steven, _____ _____ Toros.

   Toros   Hello, Steven.

   Steven   _____ , Toros.

5 **Write the conversations.**

a **David**   _____

            _____

   Alec   _____

b **Sushi**   _____

            _____

   Linda   _____

   Sushi   _____

c **Linda**   _____

            _____

   Sushi   _____

   Ben   _____

6 T4 **Write the numbers.**

Example
4 *four*

a 9 _____

b 18 _____

c 14 _____

d 12 _____

e 7 _____

f 20 _____

g 16 _____

h 5 _____

i 11 _____

j 8 _____

7 Write the numbers.

Example
1 + 1 = *two*

a 3 + 4 = _____

b 3 × 3 = _____

c 2 × 4 = _____

d 16 − 4 = _____

e 20 ÷ 2 = _____

f 3 × 6 = _____

g 12 + 8 = _____

h 19 − 2 = _____

i 18 ÷ 3 = _____

j 4 × 4 = _____

8 Complete the puzzle to make numbers.

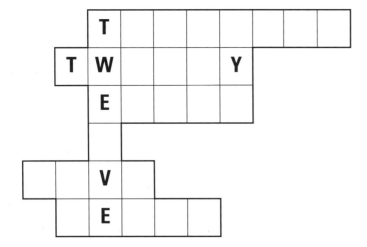

9 Find ten words → and ↓ from Unit 1.

M	T	E	N	N	I	S	N	P	A	Q
A	H	Z	L	A	M	N	Z	W	R	Y
F	I	H	A	M	B	U	R	G	E	R
G	S	E	I	E	H	H	F	D	Q	A
T	E	L	E	P	H	O	N	E	I	D
S	A	L	U	V	T	W	H	G	J	I
D	F	O	O	T	B	A	L	L	C	O

10 Translate.

a How are you?

_____

b Fine, thanks. And you?

_____

c What's your name?

_____

d My name's John.

_____

e This is a hospital.

_____

UNIT 2

Countries – *his/her* – *I/you/he/she* – *am* – *Where?* – Alphabet

1 Look at the pictures and write the countries.

a   *The United States*

b   _____

c   _____

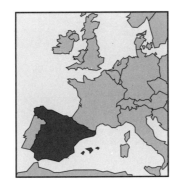

d   _____

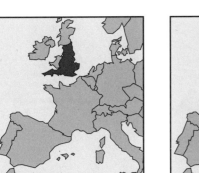

e   _____

f   _____

2 **T5** Look at the pictures and write these countries.

Hungary   Turkey   Brazil   Britain

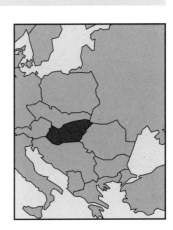

a   _____

b   _____

c   _____

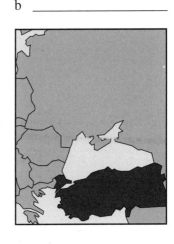

d   _____

3 `T6` **Write the countries in Britain.**

England   Scotland   Wales

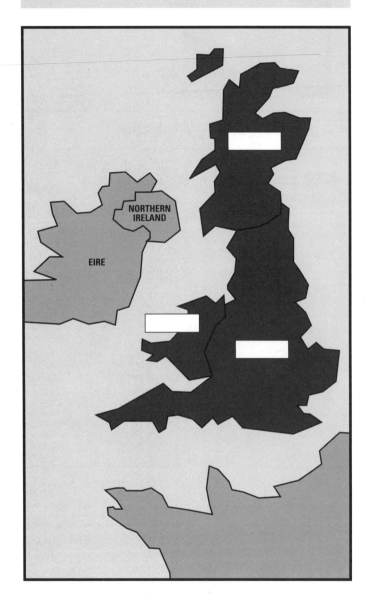

4 **Find the countries.**

Example
a i b z r l   *Brazil*

a r n f c a e   _____

b n r g h a u y   _____

c n a p a j   _____

d p n s i a   _____

e a t y l i   _____

f e a d g n l n   _____

g s n l d c a t o   _____

h r g m e n a y   _____

5 `T7` **Look at the pictures and write the questions and answers.**

a *What's his name?* _____

   His name's Jacques. _____

   Where's he from? _____

   He's from France. _____

b What's _____ name?

   Her name's _____ .

   Where's _____ from?

   She's from _____ .

c What's _____ name?

   Her name's _____ .

   Where's _____ from?

   She's from _____ .

d _____ name?

_____

_____ from?

_____ from _____ .

e _____

_____

_____

_____

f _____

_____

_____

_____

6 **T8** **Match the questions and answers.**

a What's his name?

b Where's Maria from?

c How are you?

d What's your name?

e Where are you from?

1 Fine, thanks.

2 My name's Tom.

3 His name's Steven.

4 I'm from Australia.

5 She's from Italy.

7 **T9** **Read and write.**

a **Jean** Hello. My name's Jean. _____ _____ name?
  Isabel Isabel.

  Jean Where _____ you _____ , Isabel?
  Isabel Coimbra in Portugal. And you?

  Jean _____ _____ Paris.

b **Jean** _____ , Gina. _____ are you?

  Gina _____ , thanks. And _____ ?

  Jean Very well, _____ . Gina, _____ is Isabel.

  _____ _____ Portugal.

  Gina _____ , Isabel.

  Isabel _____ , Gina.

9

8 **T 10** **Read the texts.**

This is Brigitte. She's from France. She's a teacher. Her school is in Châtres, near Paris.

This is Jamie. He's from Edinburgh, in Scotland. He's a taxi driver.

This is Sarah. Sarah's from Liverpool. She's a doctor. Her hospital is in the centre of London.

Complete the sentences.

Example
Brigitte is from *France*.

a Brigitte's a _____ .

b Her school is in _____ , near Paris.

c Jamie is from _____ .

d He's a _____ .

e Sarah's from _____ .

f Her hospital is in _____ .

9 **Write the short forms.**

Example
What is his name?
What's his name?

a My name is Tom.

_____

b I am from Italy.

_____

c You are a teacher.

_____

d What is your name?

_____

e She is from Spain.

_____

f He is a doctor.

_____

g Where is Luc from?

_____

h I am from Wales.

_____

10 Translate.

a Where are you from?

_____

b I'm from Italy.

_____

c Where's Naoko from?

_____

d She's from Japan.

_____

e Her name is Sarah. His name is Jack.

_____

_____

UNIT 3

1 `T 11` Write questions and answers.

a   *What's her job?*

   She's a doctor.

b   *What's his job?*

   He's a taxi driver.

g   _____

   _____

h   _____

   _____

c   _____

   _____

d   _____

   _____

2 Complete the puzzle to make jobs.

e   _____

   _____

f   _____

   _____

3 **T 12** Write the questions.

NAME	Alícia Diaz
COUNTRY	Spain
ADDRESS	42 c/ Martinez Campos, Salamanca
PHONE NUMBER	482 9762
AGE	23
JOB	Hairdresser
MARRIED	Yes

Example
What's her name?
Alícia Diaz.

a _____ ?
   Spain.

b _____ ?
   42 c/ Martinez Campos, Salamanca.

c _____ ?
   482 9762.

d _____ ?
   She's 23.

e _____ ?
   She's a hairdresser.

f _____ ?
   Yes, she is.

4 Answer these questions about Alícia Diaz.
Use short answers.

Example
Is Alícia from the United States?
No, she isn't.

a Is she from France?

   _____

b Is she from Spain?

   _____

c Is she 22?

   _____

d Is she 23?

   _____

e Is she a shop assistant?

   _____

f Is she a hairdresser?

   _____

g Is she married?

   _____

5 **T 13** Answer the questions about you.

a What's your name?

   _____

b Where are you from?

   _____

c What's your address?

   _____

d What's your phone number?

   _____

e How old are you?

   _____

f What's your job?

   _____

g Are you married?

   _____

6 Write questions.

Example
she/England?
Is she from England?

a he/28?

   _____

b you/doctor?

   _____

c he/married?

   _____

d I/Japan?

   _____

e she/travel agent?

   _____

f you/married?

   _____

g he/18?

   _____

h she/Italy?

   _____

7 **T 14** Match the questions to the answers.

a Is she from France?   1 Yes, he is.
b Are you married?   2 He's a taxi driver.
c What's his job?   3 Yes, I am.
d Is he a policeman?   4 No, she isn't.
e What's her job?   5 Spain.
f Where is she from?   6 She's a travel agent.

8 **Make true sentences. Put *am*, *am not*, *is*, or *is not* into the gaps.**

Example
Margaret Thatcher *is* from England.

a I _____ in class.

b Pete Sampras _____ from the United States.

c I _____ from Japan.

d Michelle Pfeiffer _____ from France.

e Madrid _____ in Spain.

f The Vatican _____ in Berlin.

g I _____ a student.

h My teacher _____ married.

9 **Write the short forms.**

Example
London is in England.
London's in England.

a Ken is not married.

_____

b Where is she from?

_____

c I am from Hungary.

_____

d I am not a policeman.

_____

e You are from Brazil.

_____

10 **Write the long forms.**

Example
He's from Scotland.
He is from Scotland.

a You aren't a housewife.

_____

b New York isn't in Italy.

_____

c The hospital's in the centre of the city.

_____

d I'm 28.

_____

e You're a travel agent.

_____

11 **T15** **Write the numbers.**

a 21   *twenty-one* _____

b 47   _____

c 60   _____

d 74   _____

e 38   _____

f 55   _____

g 100   _____

h 80   _____

i 92   _____

j 63   _____

12 **Write the numbers.**

a $23 + 26 =$ *forty-nine* _____

b $3 \times 25 =$ _____

c $100 \div 2 =$ _____

d $55 + 44 =$ _____

e $90 - 28 =$ _____

f $22 \times 3 =$ _____

g $31 + 52 =$ _____

h $54 \div 2 =$ _____

i $22 + 22 =$ _____

j $60 - 12 =$ _____

13 **Translate.**

a I'm not married.

_____

b What's your address?

_____

c Is James from Scotland?

_____

d 'How old is she?' 'I think she's twenty-six.'

_____

e Sonya isn't from France.

_____

UNIT 4

Family – Possessive 's – Who? – it/they – Classroom language

1 **T 16** Look at the family tree and complete the sentences.

Robin = Fiona
| Andrew   Susan

Example   Fiona is Robin's *wife*.

a   Andrew is Robin and Fiona's _____ .

b   Robin is Andrew and Susan's _____ .

c   Andrew is Susan's _____ .

d   Susan is Robin and Fiona's _____ .

e   Robin and Fiona are Andrew and Susan's _____ .

f   Fiona is Andrew and Susan's _____ .

g   Robin is Fiona's _____ .

h   Susan is Andrew's _____ .

i   Susan and Andrew are Robin and Fiona's _____ .

2 Are these sentences true (✔) or false (✘)? Correct the false ones.

Examples
Andrew is Susan's brother.   ✔
Fiona is Robin's sister.   ✘
Fiona is Robin's wife.

a   Susan is Andrew's sister. ☐

_____

b   Andrew and Susan are Fiona's parents. ☐

_____

c   Andrew is Susan's father. ☐

_____

d   Fiona is Susan's mother. ☐

_____

e   Robin and Fiona are Andrew's children. ☐

_____

3 **T 17** Write sentences.

a   *They're doctors.*

b   *He's a travel agent.*

c   _____

d   _____

e   _____

f   _____

g   _____

h   _____

4 **T18** Read the text and write the names on the family tree.

Elizabeth

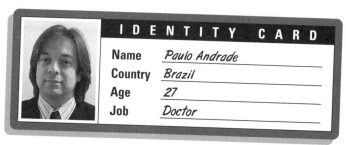

Winston is Elizabeth's husband. Winston and Elizabeth's children are Neville, Daphne, and Jessica. Neville and Daphne aren't married. Jessica is married. Her husband's name is Robert. Jessica and Robert's son is Darren.

5 Write the answers.

Example
Who's Elizabeth's husband?   *Winston.*

a   Who's Jessica's son? _____

b   Who's Daphne's brother? _____

c   Who's Winston's wife? _____

d   Who are Elizabeth and Winston's children?

  _____

e   Who's Darren's father? _____

6 Answer the questions.

Example
Who's 27? *Paulo Andrade.*

a   Who's 30? _____

b   Who's a dentist? _____

c   Who's from Hungary? _____

d   Who's a doctor? _____

e   Who's a translator? _____

f   Who's from Germany? _____

g   Who's from Brazil? _____

h   Who's 37? _____

7 Write *P* if *'s* = possession. Write *is* if *'s* = *is*.

Example
He's a teacher.   *is*
Who is George's brother?   *P*

a   Olga's 35. _____

b   Frank's son is 12. _____

c   Jack's school is in the centre of London. _____

d   Who's Pedro? _____

e   What's her job? _____

f   Jane's husband is a taxi driver. _____

g   Katy is Peter's mother. _____

h   Who are Chris's parents? _____

15

8 Make sentences. Use the words in the box.

pen football dictionary radio notebook tennis racket

Example

This is Paolo's radio.

a _____

b _____

c _____

d _____

e _____

9 Add s, 's, or ✗.

Example
My name*'s* Thérèse.

a Jane and Susan are teacher___ .

b This is the teacher___ pen.

c They are doctor___ .

d This is Vicky___ bag.

e His name ___ Chris.

f My parents ___ are in France.

10 Find the different word.

Example

book   notebook   (pen)   dictionary

a	mother	father	brother	teacher
b	fifty	twenty-two	twenty	ninety
c	am	is	are	what
d	dictionary	video	television	radio
e	taxi driver	travel agent	student	actor

11 Match the numbers and words.

26   a hundred   40   fifty-nine

twenty-eight   59   twenty-six   fourteen

31   sixty-seven   67   ninety-nine

14   99   seventy-six   100

76   forty   28   thirty-one

12 Put *is* or *are* into the gaps.

Example
Who *are* they?

a Peter _____ Kate's brother.

b Jeff and Liz _____ married.

c How _____ you?

d What _____ your job?

e They _____ my cassettes.

f Who _____ James and Sarah?

g Peter _____ Henri and Paolo's teacher.

h Robert and Maria _____ Julio's parents.

13 **T19** Put the words in the box in the correct columns.

pen   teacher   cassette   France   address
student   daughter   Japan   children   wife

•	• •	• •
pen	teacher	address
_____	_____	_____
_____	_____	_____
	_____	

14 **T20** Match a question in A with an answer in B.

A	B
What's this in English?	Certainly. Dictionary.
Sorry. Can you say it again, please?	D-I-C-T-I-O-N-A-R-Y.
Can you spell it, please?	It's a dictionary.

15 Translate.

a Simon is Katy's father.

_____

b They're teachers.

_____

c Marco and Mario aren't married.

_____

d What's your job?

_____

e Who's Tim's sister?

_____

UNIT 5

Food and drink – Present Simple (*I /you/they*) – Short answers – Requests

1 **T 21** Label the pictures.

9
14
8
4
13
11
6
7
2
12
3
5
15
1 milk
10

2 Look at the picture. Write true sentences about what you like and what you don't like.

Examples
I like wine.
I don't like meat.

a _____

b _____

c _____

d _____

e _____

f _____

g _____

h _____

3 Write five true sentences. Use the verbs in the box.

like	eat	drink	live	work

Examples
I like pop music.
I don't drink coffee.

a _____

b _____

c _____

d _____

e _____

18

4 `T 22` **Write true answers.**

Examples
Do you like oranges?
Yes, I do.
Do you like milk?
No, I don't.

a   Do you like apples?

_____

b   Do you like pizza?

_____

c   Do you like wine?

_____

d   Do you like cake?

_____

e   Do you like bananas?

_____

f   Do you like chocolate?

_____

5 `T 23` **Write true answers.**

a   Do you live in Moscow?

_____

b   Do you work in a factory?

_____

c   Do you like English?

_____

d   Do you drink tea?

_____

e   Do you eat meat?

_____

6 **Write *is*, *are*, or *do* in the gaps.**

a   '*Do* you like pizza?' 'Yes, I _____ .'

b   'Where _____ Jorge from?' 'He _____ from Spain.'

c   '_____ he a teacher?' 'Yes, he _____ .'

d   Dina and Vicky _____ hairdressers.

e   '_____ they work in a bookshop?' 'Yes, they _____ .'

f   '_____ you from France?' 'No, I'm from Germany.'

7 `T 24` **Read the text and answer the questions.**

Harry and Dave are brothers. They live in London. They work in a bank in the centre of the city. Harry is married. His wife's name is Penny. Dave is married, too. His wife is Sophie. Sophie is Penny's sister.

Harry and Dave both like football. At weekends they watch football on television, and they drink beer. Penny and Sophie don't like football. They like tennis.

Examples
Do Dave and Harry live in London?
Yes, they do.
Do they work in a factory?
No, they don't.

a   Do Dave and Harry work in a bank?

_____

b   Do they like football?

_____

c   At weekends, do they watch tennis on television?

_____

d   At weekends, do they watch football on television?

_____

e   Do they drink milk?

_____

f   Do they drink beer?

_____

g   Do Sophie and Penny like football?

_____

h   Do they like tennis?

_____

8 **Put the words in the right order.**

Example
they / London / Do / in / live ?
Do they live in London?

a like / you / pizza / Do ?

_____

b Do / hospital / work / they / in / a ?

_____

c you / drink / Do / coffee ?

_____

d live / Do / Madrid / they / in ?

_____

e eat / meat / you / Do ?

_____

9 **Write questions.**

Example
Pete and Helen work in Oxford.
Do they work in Oxford?

a They drink wine.

_____

b They eat apples.

_____

c Jorge and Maria like classical music.

_____

d Olga and Dimitra live in the centre of Rome.

_____

e They drink beer at weekends.

_____

f They work in a bank.

_____

10 **Write *is* or *are* in the gaps.**

a *Is*_____ she a secretary?

b Where _____ you from?

c What _____ this?

d What _____ your telephone number?

e Where _____ the apples?

f Where _____ she from?

g _____ they from Italy?

h Yes, they _____ .

11 **T 25** **Match a question in A with an answer in B.**

A	B
What's your name?	I'm from Italy.
Can I have a coffee, please?	Yes, they do.
Are they married?	It's my sister.
Do they like pop music?	John. John Smith.
Who's this?	Certainly. Here you are.
Are you from Germany?	Yes, they are.
What's his job?	Yes, I am.
Where are you from?	He's a doctor.

12 **T 26** **Read the conversation. Fill in the gaps.**

Frank Hello. My *name's* Frank. What's _____ name?

Marco Marco. Pleased to _____ you.

Frank Where _____ you _____, Marco?

Marco I'm from Italy. I _____ in Rome.

Frank Really? I like Rome.

Marco Where are you _____?

Frank _____ from Germany.

Marco Where in Germany?

Frank Frankfurt.

Marco What's your _____?

Frank I'm _____ teacher. And you?

Marco I _____ in a bank.

Frank _____ you like it?

Marco It's OK.

13 **Translate.**

a I like apples.

_____

b They don't drink coffee.

_____

c 'Do they work in London?' 'No, they don't.'

_____

d 'Do you like your job?' 'Yes, I do.'

_____

e 'Can I have a glass of wine, please?' 'Yes, certainly.'

_____

UNIT 6

Objects and adjectives – *a/an* – *have* – *their* – *Is this your …?* – Days of the week

1 **T 27** Write *a* or *an*.

Example
an apple
a cassette

a ___ orange   f ___ factory

b ___ radio   g ___ magazine

c ___ umbrella   h ___ exercise

d ___ answer   i ___ glass

e ___ postcard   j ___ office

2 **T 28** Answer the questions about you.

Example
Do you have a video?
Yes I do./No, I don't.

a Do you have a sister?

_____

b Do you have a computer?

_____

c Do you have an umbrella?

_____

d Do you have a notebook?

_____

e Do you have a car?

_____

f Do you have a dictionary?

_____

g Do you have a brother?

_____

3 Write questions.

Examples
you/video
Do you have a video?
they/car
Do they have a car?

a you/brother?

_____

b they/radio?

_____

c you/sister?

_____

d they/dictionary?

_____

e you/pen?

_____

f you/television?

_____

4 **T 29** Put *his*, *her*, or *their* into the gaps.

Example
'What's *his* name?' 'Robert.'

a 'What's _____ name?' 'Rafaella.'

b Hélène's a travel agent. _____ job is interesting.

c Richard and Val have a dog. _____ dog's name is Fido.

d Fernando is a teacher. _____ school is in the centre of the city.

e Alberto has a daughter. _____ name is Elena.

f 'What are _____ names?' 'Robin and Samantha.'

21

5 **T30** Put *my* or *your* into the gaps.

Example
What's *your* name?

a Hello. _____ name's Tim.

b 'Is this _____ video?' 'No, it's William's.'

c 'What's _____ job?' 'I'm a hairdresser.'

d **Kate** Jim, this is _____ friend, Bob.
Jim Pleased to meet you, Bob.
Bob Hello.

e Is that _____ mother?

6 Make sentences. Use the words in the box.

| new   old   big   small   cheap   expensive |

a *Sarah's bag is new.*   b _____

c _____   d _____

e _____   f _____

7 **T31** Read the text about Dublin. Then match the words in A with the words in B.

Dublin is a very interesting city. It is the capital city of Ireland. It is on the River Liffey. The centre of the city is old, with small streets and beautiful, old buildings. But it has new shops and restaurants, too. The food is good and the people are very friendly.

A	B
old	old buildings
good	shops
beautiful	city
friendly	centre of the city
small	streets
new	food
interesting	people

8 Write about a city you know.

_____

_____

_____

_____

_____

_____

_____

_____

9 Choose the correct sentence. Put [✓] and [✗].

Example
Have you a dictionary? [✗]
Do you have a dictionary? [✓]

1 a This is a interesting book [ ]
  b This is an interesting book. [ ]

2 a I not live in London. [ ]
  b I don't live in London. [ ]

3 a Is this your bag? [ ]
  b Is your bag? [ ]

4 a Where you work? [ ]
  b Where do you work? [ ]

5 a What's his job? [ ]
  b What's he's job? [ ]

6 a Eat you meat? [ ]
  b Do you eat meat? [ ]

10 **T 32** Write the days of the week. Put them in the correct order.

a odmyna = *Monday* [1]
b ryfadi = _____ [ ]
c dyetasu = _____ [ ]
d tyushdra = _____ [ ]
e dusayn = _____ [ ]
f dwyseeadn = _____ [ ]
g adtyrsua = _____ [ ]

11 Translate.

a It's an interesting new book.
_____

b Is this my ticket?
_____

c Can you spell it, please?
_____

d I live in an old house.
_____

e Do you have a car?
_____

12 Complete the crossword.

Across →

1 (8 letters)

3 ten – twenty – thirty – forty – ____ (5 letters)

5 'Do you ____ a car?' 'Yes, it's a Rover.' (4 letters)

6 'Do you eat meat?' '____ , I don't.' (2 letters)

7 'Can you ____ "video"?' 'Yes, I can. V-I-D-E-O.' (5 letters)

8 'What's your job?' 'I'm a ____ driver.' (4 letters)

10 (8 letters)

Down ↓

1 'What's your ____ number?' '241306.' (5 letters)

2 Can I have a cup of ____ , please? (6 letters)

4 This car is not cheap. It is ____ . (9 letters)

5 Antonella is a doctor. She works in a ____ . (8 letters)

9 This is a ____ of Britain. (3 letters)

11 New York is ____ the United States. (2 letters)

¹P	O	S	T	²C	A	R	D
		³					
							⁴
	⁵						
⁶							
	⁷						
			⁸				
		⁹					
¹⁰				¹¹			

23

STOP AND CHECK 1

1 Read. Then write the questions.

NAME	Keith Mason
AGE	34
COUNTRY	Britain
ADDRESS	32 East Road, York
PHONE NUMBER	01904 62431
MARRIED	Yes
JOB	Doctor

a *What's his name?*
His name's Keith Mason.

b _____ ?
He's from Britain.

c _____ ?
He's 34.

d _____ ?
32 East Road, York.

e _____ ?
01904 62431

f _____ ?
Yes, he is.

g _____ ?
He's a doctor.

`6`

2 Read.

Stephen and Conchita Black live in Barcelona. Conchita is from Spain, but Stephen is from England. They are travel agents. They work in the centre of the city. They like tennis and music. They have a son and a daughter. Stephen and Conchita like Barcelona. It's an interesting city and the weather is good. And they like the food!

3 Write short answers.

a Do Stephen and Conchita live in Barcelona?
Yes, they do.

b Are they travel agents?

_____

c Do they have two sons?

_____

d Do they like Barcelona?

_____

e Is the weather bad?

_____

`4`

4 Write Conchita's answers.

a Are you a travel agent?
Yes, I am.

b Are you from Italy?

_____

c Do you work in Madrid?

_____

d Do you like music?

_____

e Is Barcelona an interesting city?

_____

`4`

5 Read the conversation. Fill in the gaps with the words in the box.

on	have	yes	your	are	I'm	do

In school

Osman Hello . My name's Osman. What's _____ name?

Sue Sue. Where _____ you from, Osman?

Osman _____ from Turkey.

Sue When do you _____ English lessons?

Osman _____ Thursday evenings.

Sue _____ you like English?

Osman _____ , I do.

`7`

6 Put the words in the correct box.

Monday   big   sandwich   tea   hospital
Wednesday   mother   interesting   Tuesday
apple   hotel   chocolate   father   beer   salad
Friday   friendly   wine   sister   coffee
Saturday   small   wife   school   cheap   bank
meat   milk   factory   daughter

Days	Food	Drink	Family	Places	Adjectives
Monday					

`30`

UNIT 7

Activities – *like* + *-ing* – Present Simple negative (*I/you/we/they*) –
Telling the time

1 **T 33** Label the activities.

a   *playing tennis*

b _____

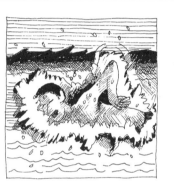

g _____

h _____

c _____

d _____

i _____

j _____

e _____

f _____

2 Write true sentences.

Examples
I like playing tennis.
I don't like dancing.

a _____

b _____

c _____

d _____

e _____

f _____

g _____

25

3 Make the sentences negative.

Examples
I work in London.
I don't work in London.
We are teachers.
We aren't teachers.

a   We go to work on Saturdays.

_____

b   We are policemen.

_____

c   I have an expensive car.

_____

d   We go to church on Sundays.

_____

e   They like listening to music in the evenings.

_____

f   You like playing tennis.

_____

4 Make the sentences positive.

Examples
We don't like dancing.
We like dancing.
We aren't doctors.
We are doctors.

a   I don't drink milk.

_____

b   We aren't married.

_____

c   You don't work on Mondays.

_____

d   They don't have a new television.

_____

e   We don't like swimming.

_____

f   They don't like going out in the evenings.

_____

5   T 34   Write questions with *when*. Then write true answers.

Example
you/read?
When do you read?
I read at weekends.

a   you/like eating in restaurants?

_____

_____

b   you/go to school/work?

_____

_____

c   you/go swimming?

_____

_____

d   you/go out with friends?

_____

_____

e   you/have English lessons?

_____

_____

6   Complete the sentences with *in*, *on*, *at*, or *to*.

Example
On Mondays I go out with my friends.

a   I live ___ Oxford.
b   ___ weekends I play tennis.
c   What do you do ___ Saturdays?
d   I go out with my friends ___ the evenings.
e   I don't like listening ___ music.
f   ___ Wednesday afternoons I go swimming.
g   What do they do ___ the mornings?
h   ___ Saturday mornings I go ___ the supermarket.
i   We like staying ___ home.
j   Do you like eating ___ restaurants?

7 `T 35` **Read about Simon and Danka Wilson.**

NAMES	Simon and Danka Wilson
FROM	He – England She – Poland
HOME	Flat in Warsaw
FAMILY	Two daughters
JOBS	He – English teacher She – travel agent
HOBBIES	Eating in restaurants. Reading.

Simon Wilson writes:

I'm from England and my wife, Danka, is from Poland. We live in a flat in Warsaw. We have two daughters. I'm a teacher and Danka is a travel agent. We like eating in restaurants and reading.

8 `T 36` **Write about Moira and Pablo Borrero.**

NAMES	Moira and Pablo Borrero
FROM	She – Ireland He – Columbia
HOME	Small house in Dublin
FAMILY	One son
JOBS	She – doctor He – Spanish teacher
HOBBIES	Cooking. Dancing.

Moira Borrero writes:

I'm from Ireland and _____

_____

_____

_____

_____

_____

_____

_____

9 `T 37` **Write the times.**

It's three o'clock.   _____

_____ _____ _____ _____

10 Draw the times.

It's four o'clock.   It's ten past nine.

It's quarter past one.   It's half past seven.

It's twenty-five to six.   It's quarter to eleven.

11 Translate.

a   I like eating in restaurants.

   _____

b   Luis and Gina don't like listening to music.

   _____

c   When do you learn English?

   _____

d   'What's the time, please?' 'It's quarter to six.'

   _____

e   We aren't from London. We're from Manchester.

   _____

12 T38   Read the text.

Hello. I'm Hiroko Murata. This is my sister. Her name is Tomoko. We live in Ichinomiya with our parents, but we don't work in Ichinomiya. We work in Nagoya. Nagoya is a big city near Ichinomiya. I am a travel agent and my sister is a nurse. We work on Saturdays but we don't work on Sundays.

In the evenings my parents like reading, but my sister and I don't. We like listening to music. My mother and father like playing tennis at weekends, but Tomoko and I don't. We like watching television!

Make true sentences for Hiroko and Tomoko.

Example
live in Ichinomiya
We live in Ichinomiya.
work in Ichinomiya
We don't work in Ichinomiya.

a   work on Saturdays

   _____

b   work on Sundays

   _____

c   like reading in the evenings

   _____

d   like listening to music

   _____

e   like playing tennis at weekends

   _____

f   like watching television

   _____

UNIT 8

Present Simple (*he/she/it*) – Short answers – Social English 1

1 **T 39** **What do they do? Put the sentences in the box in the correct columns.**

He reads newspapers a lot.	He trains a lot.	He plays matches.
He drives to work.	He sometimes works at night.	He meets a lot of people.
He has a computer.	He drives a lot.	He works at home.

He's a journalist.	He's a footballer.	He's a taxi driver.
He reads newspapers a lot.		

2 **Complete the sentences with *do* or *does*.**

Example
Does she live in London?

a   When _____ Harry arrive at work?

b   _____ you like whisky?

c   When _____ you have dinner?

d   _____ she play tennis?

e   Where _____ they live?

f   Where _____ he live?

g   _____ you drive?

h   _____ he like swimming?

3 **Choose the correct verb.**

Example
John (*lives*)/live in London.

a   At weekends Ali *cook/cooks* dinner for his friends.

b   Michelle *have/has* lunch at work.

c   Ian and Rachel *drive/drives* to work.

d   What does your husband *do/does*?

e   When *does/do* you get up?

f   Rita does not *have/has* breakfast.

g   Andrew and I *like/likes* playing tennis.

4 **Look at the information about Karen and Paul.**

Does he/she ...	Karen	Paul
like cooking?	✗	✔
like whisky?	✗	✔
eat meat?	✔	✔
have breakfast	✔	✗
drive to work?	✗	✗
like his/her job?	✗	✔

Write short answers to the questions.

Example
Does Karen like cooking?
No, she doesn't.
Does Paul like cooking?
Yes, he does.

a   Does Karen eat meat?

_____

b   Does Paul drive to work?

_____

c   Does Paul like his job?

_____

d   Does Karen like whisky?

_____

e   Does Paul eat meat?

_____

f   Does Karen like her job?

_____

g   Does Paul have breakfast?

_____

h   Does Karen drive to work?

_____

5 **Complete the sentences about Karen and Paul.**

Example
Karen *eats* meat.

a   Karen _____ breakfast.
b   Paul _____ cooking.
c   Paul _____ whisky.
d   Karen _____ meat.
e   Paul _____ his job.

6 **T 40** **Fill in the gaps with the correct form of the verb in brackets.**

Karen Fisher says:

I *live* (live) in Japan with my husband, Paul. I
am (be) a teacher, and Paul _____ (be) a
journalist. We _____ (live) in a flat near the centre
of Tokyo. It _____ (be) very expensive. Paul
_____ (work) at home. He _____ (read) and
_____ (write) a lot. He _____ (have) a computer.
I _____ (work) in a language school in Tokyo. We
_____ (have) a car, but I don't _____ (drive) to
work. I _____ (walk). At weekends, Paul _____
(play) football, and I _____ (go) swimming. On
Saturday evenings, we _____ (go) to the cinema,
or sometimes we _____ (cook) dinner for our
friends.

7 **Write short answers. Use *do*, *does*, *don't*, or *doesn't*.**

Example
Do you like playing football?
Yes, I *do*.

a   Does he leave home at eight o'clock?

No, he _____ .

b   Do you like milk?

Yes, I _____ .

c   Do Edwardo and Conchita play tennis at weekends?

No, they _____ .

d   Does Elizabeth work in Oxford?

No, she _____ .

e   Does Ivan like his job?

Yes, he _____ .

f   Do you cook dinner for your friends at weekends?

No, I _____ .

g   Do they arrive at work at nine o'clock?

Yes, they _____ .

h   Does Tania usually stay at home on Mondays?

Yes, she _____ .

8 **T 41** Read about Lee and Tracy. Write questions and answers.

	Lee	Tracy
get up	6.30	7.45
go to work	7.15	9.00
have lunch	12.30	1.10
arrive home	4.20	5.35

Examples
When does Lee get up?
He gets up at half past six.
When does Tracy have lunch?
She has lunch at ten past one.

a _____

_____

b _____

_____

c _____

_____

d _____

_____

e _____

_____

f _____

_____

9 Label the pictures using words from the box.

plane   bus   car   bike   motorbike   train   ship

a *ship* ____   b _____   c _____   d _____

e _____   f _____   g _____

10 **T 42** Complete the conversations. Use the words from the box.

I'm sorry.   Excuse me.

1 **A** *Excuse me* ____ . Is your name Nina?
  B No, it isn't.
  A Oh, _____ .
  B It's OK.

2 **C** _____ .
  D Yes?
  C Can you tell me the time, please?
  D It's one o'clock.
  C Thanks.

3 **E** _____ .
  Can you tell me the time, please?
  F _____ .
  I don't know.
  E Thanks, anyway.

11 Translate.

a Osman never goes shopping at weekends.

_____

b 'Does Idoia live in London?' 'No, she doesn't.'

_____

c When does Tomás arrive at work?

_____

d She goes to London by train.

_____

e At weekends he has breakfast at half past nine.

_____

31

UNIT 9

Daily routines – Present Simple negative (*he/she/it*) – Question words – Social English 2

1 **T 43** Look at the pictures and complete the sentences about Kevin's day.

a Kevin *gets up* at *half past seven* .

b He _____ at eight o'clock.

c He _____ home at _____ .

d He _____ students in a university.

e He _____ a sandwich for lunch.

f He _____ the university at _____ .

g He _____ home at five o'clock.

2 **Match a question word in A with an answer in B.**

A	B
a Where …?	1 At nine o'clock.
b What …?	2 Pierre.
c When …?	3 In Rome.
d Who …?	4 Because he doesn't have a car.
e Why …?	5 He's a policeman.

3 **T 44** **Make questions. Then choose answers from B.**

Example
live / where / Maria / does ?
Where does Maria live? Answer: 3

a Saturdays / on / who / works ?

_____ Answer: _____

b do / what / Oliver / does ?

_____ Answer: _____

c he / work / why / walk / does / to ?

_____ Answer: _____

d home / does / when / she / leave ?

_____ Answer: _____

4 **T 45** **Read the text and answer the questions.**

Justin Walker is a hairdresser. He lives in Glasgow. He gets up at half past seven and has a cup of coffee. He doesn't have breakfast. He leaves home at quarter past eight. He doesn't have a car. He takes the bus to work. He starts work at ten to nine. He likes his job because he likes talking to people. At twelve o'clock he has lunch in a small restaurant. He leaves work at five o'clock. In the evenings he likes reading and listening to music. At weekends he visits his mother. She lives in Edinburgh.

a What does Justin do?

He's a hairdresser.

b Where does he live?

_____

c When does he get up?

_____

d Why does he like his job?

_____

e Who does he visit at weekends?

_____

5 **Complete the sentences about Justin.**

Example
He *doesn't have* breakfast.

a He _____ a car.

b He _____ work at ten to ten.

c He _____ lunch at home.

d He _____ his brother at weekends.

e His mother _____ in Glasgow.

6 **Write about you. Use the words in the box.**

live get up have breakfast go to school/work start work have lunch like/don't like leave school/work at weekends in the evenings

_____
_____
_____
_____
_____
_____
_____
_____
_____
_____
_____
_____

7 Choose the correct verb.

Example

Juan doesn't (like)/likes teaching children.

a Lucia doesn't *like/likes* swimming.

b Kurt doesn't *have/has* a car.

c Karl and Jo *lives/live* in New York.

d Where *does/do* Jorge teach?

e Who does Harry *visit/visits* at weekends?

f Mandy doesn't *get up/gets up* early.

g Why does Lucio *like/likes* his job?

8 Make these sentences negative.

Examples
Andreas lives in Britain.
Andreas doesn't live in Britain.
Kristina's a teacher.
Kristina isn't a teacher.

a The train leaves at quarter to one.

_____

b Raoul goes to work by bike.

_____

c Ramiro and Raquel eat eggs for breakfast.

_____

d Lorena's sister's a travel agent.

_____

e Piet leaves work at half past four.

_____

f Oliver and Neville like playing tennis.

_____

g This book is very interesting.

_____

h Lídia works in a bank.

_____

i We are policemen.

_____

j Erol is married.

_____

9 Make these sentences positive.

Example
Jed doesn't have breakfast at seven o'clock.
Jed has breakfast at seven o'clock.

a Lolita doesn't like working in a bank.

_____

b Manuel and Pilar don't go out at weekends.

_____

c They aren't from Britain.

_____

d Chris doesn't leave work at six o'clock.

_____

e His name isn't Stefan.

_____

f Lourdes doesn't have a television.

_____

g The school isn't in the centre of the city.

_____

h Martin and Anne don't like their jobs.

_____

10 Fill in the gaps with prepositions from the box.

at	on	at	for	to
in	on	at	for	

a I live *in*_____ London.

b Lorenzo works _____ home.

c I leave home _____ six o'clock.

d I have eggs _____ breakfast.

e Enzo watches films _____ television.

f I go swimming _____ Mondays.

g Chantal visits her parents _____ weekends.

h When do you go _____ bed?

i Ahmed works _____ IBM.

11 **T 46** **Fill in the gaps in the conversations.**

Sue _Hello_, Pete.

Pete Hello, Sue. _____ to see _____.

Sue And you. _____'s work?

Pete Oh, not _____.

Nick Goodbye, Pam.

Pam _____, Nick. _____ a _____ weekend!

Nick Thanks, Pam. _____ to you.

Pam _____. See you _____ Monday.

12 **Write the opposite. Use the words in the box.**

father	play	leave	go to bed	she
early	old	stop	sister	expensive

a he   _she_   f arrive   _____

b get up _____   g work   _____

c start   _____   h brother _____

d new   _____   i late   _____

e mother _____   j cheap   _____

13 **Translate.**

a When does Bob get up?

_____

b Craig doesn't like dancing.

_____

c What do you have for breakfast?

_____

d What do you do?

_____

e 'Why do you like your job?' 'Because I like teaching children.'

_____

_____

14 **Crossword.**

Across →

1 Hans is a doctor. He _works_ in a hospital. (5 letters)

3 two – four – ____ – eight – ten. (3 letters)

4 _____ do you like your job? (3 letters)

5 My father teaches in a ____ ____ . (9 letters & 6 letters)

6 I like my job because it is very ____ . (11 letters)

8 José doesn't get up ____ . He gets up at 11 o'clock. (5 letters)

10 Not cheap. (9 letters)

11 'When do you have breakfast?' 'I ____ have breakfast at 8 o'clock.' (7 letters)

Down ↓

2 We ____ work at 3 o'clock and have a cup of tea. (4 letters)

3 When do you ____ work in the morning? (5 letters)

4 '____'s that?' 'It's my brother, Simon.' (3 letters)

5 Do you ____ French? (5 letters)

7 six – ____ – eighteen – twenty-four. (6 letters)

9 Andrea ____ work at seven o'clock in the evening. (6 letters)

UNIT 10

Houses, rooms, and furniture – Colours – *There is/are* – *any* – At the post office

1 **T 47** **Look at the picture. Write the names.**

A *living room*

B _____

C _____

D _____

E _____

F _____

2 **T48** Match the word in the box to the number in the picture.

toilet	picture	television	bed	tree	
chair	fridge	cat	car	bath	lamp
bicycle	armchair	cooker	sofa	table	

1 _television_ _____ 9 _____

2 _____ 10 _____

3 _____ 11 _____

4 _____ 12 _____

5 _____ 13 _____

6 _____ 14 _____

7 _____ 15 _____

8 _____ 16 _____

3 Look at the picture. Make eight sentences with *There is …* and *There are …*

Examples
There are two armchairs in the living room.
There's a car in the garden.

a _____

b _____

c _____

d _____

e _____

f _____

g _____

h _____

4 Write short answers.

Examples
Is there a television in the living room?
Yes, there is.
Are there any cats in the living room?
No, there aren't.

a Is there a table in the kitchen?

_____

b Are there any chairs in the bathroom?

_____

c Is there a sofa in the living room?

_____

d Are there any dogs in the garden?

_____

e Is there a tree in the garden?

_____

f Are there any armchairs in the living room?

_____

5 **T49** Write six questions and answers.

Examples
fridge/living room?
Is there a fridge in the living room? No, there isn't.
flowers/dining room?
Are there any flowers in the dining room? Yes, there are.

a television/living room? _____

_____

_____

b chairs/kitchen? _____

_____

_____

c cats/garden? _____

_____

_____

d television/dining room? _____

_____

_____

e armchairs/bedroom? _____

_____

_____

f table/dining room? _____

_____

_____

6 **T50** Match a question in A with an answer in B.

A	B
Is Manolo in the living room?	Yes, there are.
Is there a table in the garden?	No, he isn't.
Is this your pencil?	Yes, they are.
Is Corinne from Britain?	No, there isn't.
Are there any flowers on the table?	Yes, it is.
Are Kim and Frances married?	No, she isn't.

7 `T 51` **What colour is it? Write the colours from the box.**

black	yellow	green	grey	white	brown	orange	blue	red

1 _yellow_

2 _____

3 _____

4 _____

5 _____

6 _____

7 _____

8 `T 52` **Read the text and answer the questions.**

OUR HOUSE

We live in a small, old house in Guildford. It has two bedrooms, a living room, a dining room, a kitchen – and there's a bathroom, of course!

In the living room there are two blue armchairs and a red sofa. We also have a television, a video, and a CD player. On the wall there are two pictures. In the evenings we sit in the living room and watch television or listen to music.

In the dining room there is a table and four chairs. There are always flowers on the table. The kitchen is new: there is a cooker, a fridge, and a table. We have breakfast in the kitchen, but we have lunch and dinner in the dining room.

We have a beautiful garden. There are a lot of flowers and two trees. Our cats like playing in the garden. We are very happy in our house!

a Where do William and Lucy live?

They live in a small, old house in Guildford.

b Does their house have two bedrooms?

_____

c What colour are the armchairs?

_____

d Is there a sofa in the living room?

_____

e What do William and Lucy do in the evenings?

_____

f Is the kitchen old?

_____

g Where do William and Lucy have lunch?

_____

h Are there any trees in the garden?

_____

i Are William and Lucy happy in their house?

_____

9 **Write about your home.**

_____

_____

_____

_____

_____

10 Fill in the gaps. Use words from the box.

in	at	on	in	at	on	in	from
on	by	for	in				

a I play football _on___ Saturdays.

b Do you play tennis _____ weekends?

c Is there a sofa _____ the living room?

d There are two magazines _____ the chair.

e Where are you _____ ?

f What do you have _____ breakfast?

g I leave the house _____ eight o'clock.

h Ramona goes to work _____ bus.

i I always go swimming _____ the mornings.

j Sharon Stone lives _____ the USA.

k There are flowers _____ the table _____ the living room.

11 **T 53** Put the words in the box in the correct column.

kitchen	lovely	Tuesday	assistant	cassette
secondary	interesting	banana	afternoon	
antique	secretary	children		

●.	.●	●..	.●.	..●
kitchen				

12 Translate.

a There's a table in the dining room.

_____

b There are three armchairs in the living room.

_____

c 'Is there a tree in the garden?' 'Yes, there is.'

_____

d 'Are there any flowers on the table?' 'No, there aren't.'

_____

e 'What colour is the bedroom?' 'It's yellow.'

_____

13 **T 54** Put the sentences in the correct order to make a conversation.

AT THE POST OFFICE

☐ Here you are … Thank you.

☐ Afternoon.

☐ That's 85p, please.

1 Good afternoon.

☐ Thank you.

☐ I'd like these envelopes, please.

14 **T 55** Fill in the gaps in the conversation.

A Good morning.

B Morning.

A _____ I _____ three first class stamps, _____ ?

B Certainly. _____ 75p, please.

A _____ you are … _____ you.

B _____ .

UNIT 11

Prices – *How much is/are ...? – Can I have ...? –* In a café

1 [T 56] **Answer the questions.**

CDs SPECIAL OFFERS

ELTON JOHN'S Greatest Hits	£11.99
JULIO IGLESIAS Love Songs	£10.99
SIMPLY RED – Picture Box	£9.50
REM – Out of Time	£9.75
THE BEATLES Abbey Road	£10.99
EAGLES – Hotel California	£11.99
BOB DYLAN'S Greatest Hits	£7.85
The Best of ELLA FITZGERALD	£6.59
MOZART SYMPHONIES 39 & 40	£4.99
BACH St Matthew Passion	£15.75
VIVALDI The Four Seasons	£5.30

VIDEO CASSETTES
3 CASSETTES £4.99

BARGAINS JAZZ Classical POP

5 CASSETTES
C 60 £7.50
C 90 £9.90

VIDEOS £9.99 each

OPERA

Examples
How much is the Julio Iglesias CD?
It's £10.99.
How much are the C60 cassettes?
They're £7.50.

a How much is the 'Simply Red Live!' video?

_____

b How much are the C90 cassettes?

_____

c How much is the Ella Fitzgerald CD?

_____

d How much are the video cassettes?

_____

e How much is the Dire Straits video?

_____

f How much is the Vivaldi CD?

_____

2 Match the prices and the words.

17p   two pounds ninety-nine   58p

five p   £26.47   fifteen pounds fifty-five

75p   £6.49   forty three p

six pounds forty-nine   £99

one pound sixty-eight   £1.68   sixty p

five pounds seventy-two   £2.99   5p

three pounds eighty-one   43p

ninety-eight p   £5.72   seventy-five p

seventeen p   £3.81

98p   fifty-eight p   £15.55

ninety-nine pounds

60p   twenty-six pounds forty-seven

3 Write the answers.

Example
£3.42 + 42p = *three pounds eighty-four*
10p + 21p = *thirty-one p*

a   £1.38 + £2 = _____

b   98p + 6p = _____

c   £6.30 + £3.70 = _____

d   47p + 47p = _____

e   £10.50 + £1.48 = _____

f   17p + 32p = _____

g   £72 + £19.20 = _____

h   £1.06 + £1.08 = _____

i   82p + 6p = _____

j   £42.30 + £23.20 = _____

4 **T 57** Complete the conversations with the words in the box.

Good morning.   Can I have   How much are
No, thanks.   Anything else?   I'm sorry.
Can I help you?   How much is
That's £15.20, please.   Good afternoon.

A *Good morning.* _____

B Good morning. _____ five
C60 cassettes, please?

A Here you are. _____
B No, thanks.
A That's £7.50, please.

C Good afternoon.

D _____ Can I help you?
C Yes. Can I have the 'Simply Red Live!' video,
please?
D Certainly. Here you are.

C _____ that?
D £9.99, please. Anything else?
C Yes. A CD, please. Do you have 'Sergeant Pepper'
by The Beatles?

D No, we don't. _____ But
we have 'Abbey Road'.
C No, thanks. I have 'Abbey Road'.
D Anything else?

C _____

E Good afternoon.

F Good afternoon. _____

E _____ the C90 cassettes?
F £9.90 for five.
E OK. Five, please.
F Anything else?
E Yes. A CD. Vivaldi's 'Four Seasons'.
F Here you are. £9.90 and £5.30.

_____

5 [T58] **Conversation in a café. Number the lines in the correct order.**

Waiter	Customer
☐ That's £4.10.	☐ Yes. Can I have a ham salad, please?
☐ Certainly. Here you are. Anything else?	☐ Here you are … Thanks.
[1] Good evening. Can I help you?	☐ Yes. An orange juice.
☐ Thanks.	

6 [T59] **Put the words in the correct order to make sentences or questions. Then use them to complete the conversation.**

help / can / I / you
to / anything / drink
you / here / are
much / that / how / is
please / have / sandwich / can / a / I / ham

Waiter   Good morning. (a) *Can I help you?*

Customer Good morning. Can I have the menu, please?

Waiter   Certainly. (b) _____

_____

Customer Thanks. (c) _____

_____

Waiter   One ham sandwich. (d) _____

_____

Customer Yes. A cup of tea, please.

Waiter   OK.

Customer (e) _____

Waiter   £2.70, please.

Customer Here you are.

Waiter   Thank you.

7 **Look at the menu. Make a conversation between the waiter and a customer.**

Menu

SANDWICHES		DESSERTS	
egg	1.60	piece of cake	1.30
ham	1.80	piece of apple pie	1.50
cheese	1.50	ice-cream	1.00
cheese & tomato	1.70	**DRINKS**	
SALADS		cup of tea	90p
ham	3.20	cup of coffee	1.20
egg	3.00	coke	80p
cheese	3.10	milk	80p
HOT FOOD		orange juice	90p
pizza	3.30	mineral water	70p
hamburger	2.60		
chips	1.00		

Waiter   _____

Customer _____

_____

_____

_____

_____

_____

_____

_____

_____

_____

_____

8 **Complete the sentences with a negative.**

Example
I like coffee, but *I don't like tea.*

a I have a television, but _____

_____

b Antonella likes going to the cinema, but _____

_____

c Robert likes apples, but _____

_____

d They like playing football, but _____

_____

e Rachel has a dog, but _____

_____

9 **Put the words in the correct columns.**

apple pie   baker   bank   bathroom
bedroom   black   blue   chips   dentist
dining room   factory   green
ham salad   hospital   journalist   kitchen
living room   nurse   orange juice
post office   red   restaurant   sandwich
secretary   shop assistant   tea
travel agency   white   yellow

10 **Translate.**

a How much are the brown envelopes?

_____

b Can I have a ham sandwich, please?

_____

c Here you are.

_____

d How much is that?

_____

11 **Put *a*, *the*, or ✘ in the gaps.**

Examples
She is *a* doctor.
I don't eat ✘ meat.
He watches television in *the* evenings.

a Julia doesn't like _____ coffee.

b Can I have _____ cup of coffee, please?

c Julio and Laura are _____ teachers.

d I like playing tennis in _____ mornings.

e Philippe is _____ secretary.

f Helmut works in _____ bookshop.

g Kath likes listening to _____ music.

h When do you go to _____ supermarket?

i I don't eat in _____ restaurants.

Food & drink	Colours	Jobs	Rooms	Places
apple pie				

UNIT 12

Seasons – Months – Adverbs of frequency – Prepositions – At the bank

1 **T 60** Find the months. Then put them in the correct order.

a r a y u j a n   *January*   ☐ *1*

b l u j y   _____   ☐

c l a i p r   _____   ☐

d d e m e b e r c   _____   ☐

e r c o b o e t   _____   ☐

f y b r f r e a u   _____   ☐

g b e m e p e s t r   _____   ☐

h n u e j   _____   ☐

i t u u a s g   _____   ☐

j a h m c r   _____   ☐

k e r b n e o m v   _____   ☐

l y a m   _____   ☐

2 Write the seasons.

a When is it hot? *summer*

b When do the flowers begin to grow? _____

c When does it snow? _____

d When are the trees yellow, red, and gold? _____

3 **T 61** Read the text and match the pictures with parts of the letter.

In the summer holidays, <u>Kate and Mike Green and their children, Josh and Edwina</u>, go to the beach for two or three weeks. They always go to Hastings in the south of England. They usually stay in a small house or a flat by the sea, but sometimes they stay in a hotel.

Every morning they go to the beach. Joshua goes swimming but he doesn't stay in the water very long because it's very cold! Edwina never swims. She plays on the beach.

They usually have sandwiches for lunch or sometimes they go to a small café. In the afternoons they walk in the Old Town or in the park. In the evenings they often go to the cinema or the theatre.

4 Put the correct word from the box in the gaps.

always   usually   often   sometimes   never

a   Kate, Mike, and their children _always_ go to Hastings in the summer.

b   They _____ go to the theatre in the evenings.

c.   Edwina _____ swims in the sea.

d   They _____ have lunch in a café.

e   They _____ stay in a small house or a flat by the sea.

5 Put the words in the correct order to make sentences and questions.

Example
in summer / usually / We / to the beach / go
We usually go to the beach in summer.

a   often / at weekends / goes out / Liz / for dinner

   _____

b   to the cinema / you / go / Do / often ?

   _____

c   go / for two weeks / I / to France / sometimes / in July

   _____

d   drive / We / work / never / to

   _____

e   with you / she / have / Does / lunch / usually ?

   _____

f   on Saturdays / Silvio / goes dancing / usually / with Leontina

   _____

g   learn / at weekends / Does / English / Henri ?

   _____

h   usually / Is / cold / it / in November ?

   _____

6 Write sentences about you. Use the words in the box.

always   usually   often   sometimes   never

Example
I always get up at 6.30 on Mondays.

a   _____

b   _____

c   _____

d   _____

e   _____

7 Write *do* or *does* in the gaps.

Example
Chris *does*n't like tennis.

a   Where _____ you usually go in summer?

b   They _____ n't often eat in restaurants.

c   Why _____ Simon always stay at home in the evenings?

d   When _____ she usually get home?

e   I _____ n't often go skiing.

8   T 62   Choose the different sound.

Example

live   sit   (like)   it

a	thank	family	and	day
b	go	know	love	coke
c	new	when	never	February
d	in	I	spring	sister
e	family	my	usually	agency
f	play	Tuesday	United States	dance
g	usually	up	lunch	much

45

9 **T 63** **Read about Kathy.**

I like spring. The trees are green and it is warm again. I live in a small village in the country. I often go cycling in spring.

In summer I go on holiday. I usually go to Italy or Spain with my family. It's always hot there. I like going to the beach and swimming in the sea.

Autumn is my favourite season. It is cold but it isn't wet. There are woods near my village and I often go walking there with my brother and sister.

I don't like winter. It is very cold, wet, and grey. I don't often go out in the evenings. I usually stay at home and watch television or listen to music.

Are the sentences true (✔) or false (✘) ?

Example
Kathy doesn't like spring. ✘

a   Kathy never goes cycling in spring. ☐

b   Kathy likes going to the beach in spring. ☐

c   In summer Kathy usually goes to Italy or Spain. ☐

d   In autumn it is cold and wet. ☐

e   In winter Kathy often goes out in the evenings. ☐

f   Kathy doesn't like winter. ☐

10 Now you write about the seasons.

Spring

_____

_____

_____

_____

_____

Summer

_____

_____

_____

_____

_____

Autumn

_____

_____

_____

_____

_____

Winter

_____

_____

_____

_____

_____

11 Put the correct words from the box in the gaps.

warm   wet   cold   hot

a It's _____ .   c It's _____ .

b It's _____ .   d It's _____ .

12 Label the pictures with words from the box.

rain   snow   sun   wind   fog

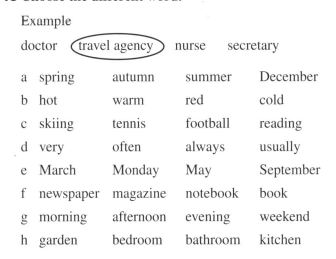

a _____   b _____

c _____   d _____

e _____

13 Choose the different word.

Example

doctor   (travel agency)   nurse   secretary

a	spring	autumn	summer	December
b	hot	warm	red	cold
c	skiing	tennis	football	reading
d	very	often	always	usually
e	March	Monday	May	September
f	newspaper	magazine	notebook	book
g	morning	afternoon	evening	weekend
h	garden	bedroom	bathroom	kitchen

14 [T 64] Put the sentences in the correct order to make a conversation.

☐ Yes. Can I change some traveller's cheques, please?

☐ Here you are.

☑ Good morning. Can I help you?

☐ Can I see your passport, please?

☐ Yes, of course. How much do you want to change?

☐ Thank you. Goodbye.

☐ £80.

☐ Thank you. Can you sign here, please? … That's twenty, forty, sixty, eighty pounds.

15 Translate the sentences.

a In summer I often go out with my friends.

_____

b In winter I usually go skiing in Scotland.

_____

c 'Do you get up early?' 'Yes, sometimes.'

_____

d 'When's your birthday?' 'It's in July.'

_____

e I never get up early at weekends.

_____

47

STOP AND CHECK 2

1 Read the text and answer the questions.

David and Lucy Smith live in Blackpool, in England. They have a big house near the beach. There are five bedrooms, two bathrooms, and a balcony. David and Lucy have two children. Their names are Sam and Anne. Sam is twelve and Anne is fourteen.

David works in a bank and Lucy is a doctor. They get up at seven o'clock every morning. They usually leave home at eight o'clock. Lucy drives to school with Sam and Anne, and then she drives to work at the hospital.

In the evenings David always cooks dinner. After dinner David and Lucy sometimes watch television. They never go out in the evenings. Sam and Anne visit their friends.

In summer they go to the beach at weekends. Sam and Anne like swimming in the sea. In winter they don't go to the beach at weekends because it's very cold.

a Where do David and Lucy live?
   They live in Blackpool, in England.
b What does Lucy do?

   _____

c When do they get up?

   _____

d Who do Sam and Anne visit?

   _____

e In summer, where do they go at weekends?

   _____

f Why don't they go to the beach in winter?

   _____   **5**

2 Answer the questions.

a Does David work in a post office?
   No, he doesn't.
b Do David and Lucy watch television after dinner?
   Yes, sometimes.
c Are there five bedrooms in their house?

   _____

d Do they leave home at eight o'clock?

   _____

e Does Lucy drive to work?

   _____

f Does David cook dinner?

   _____

g Do they go out in the evenings?

   _____

h Do Sam and Anne like swimming?

   _____   **6**

3 Read the conversation. Fill in the gaps with words from the box.

| hello | no | at | on | of | how | on | when |
| an | to | at | not | help | has | good | a | else |

In a restaurant

Ivan *Hello*, Pilar.
Pilar Hi, Ivan. Nice _____ see you.
Ivan And you. _____'s work?
Pilar Oh, _____ bad, thanks. Where's Enzo?
Ivan He's _____ school. He always _____ English lessons _____ Thursdays.
Pilar Of course.
Waiter _____ evening. Can I _____ you?
Ivan Can I have _____ cup _____ tea, please?
Pilar And can I have _____ orange juice?
Waiter Anything _____ ?
Ivan _____, thanks.
Pilar There's a good film _____ television this evening: *Long Summer Days*.
Ivan _____ does it start?
Pilar _____ seven o'clock.   **16**

4 Put the letters in the correct order to make words.

Months	Bank	Seasons	Food & drink
eujn *June*	odpun *pound*	ertiwn _____	ofecef _____
rafberuy _____	yenmo _____	mutanu _____	dalas _____
crooetb _____	evelratlr's/ ehqceu _____	gispnr _____	namriel/ atewr _____

Colours	Rooms	Furniture
lube _____	leitot _____	rachimar _____
reneg _____	icnketh _____	asof _____
wobnr _____	gliniv/omor _____	lateb _____

19